D0295117

For my beautiful Victoria

HarperCollins*Publishers*
77–85 Fulham Palace Road,
Hammersmith, London W6 8JB

www.harpercollins.co.uk

First published by HarperCollins*Publishers* 2009
2

© Giles Andreae 2009

Giles Andreae asserts the moral right
to be identified as the author of this work

A catalogue record of this book
is available from the British Library

ISBN-13 978 0 00 731061 6

Printed and bound in China by Leo Paper Products Limited

I LOVE YOU

You are a Chocolate Button of **LOVELINESS** on the great Caramel Pudding of **LIFE**

The CHOCOLATE BUTTON of LOVELINESS

I ADORE YOU

I ADORE you, you crazy, gorgeous, WONDERFUL (but also sometimes quite WEIRD -but still very LOVELY) person.

Nothing is **BIG** enough to hold my **LOVE** for you. Not even the holy teacup of the GIANT Space Monkey.

The HOLY TEACUP

PET NAMES

When people fall in LOVE,
they give each other really
EMBARRASSING Pet Names.
The more they LOVE each other,
the more EMBARRASSING the names.
That must mean I LOVE you
a whole lot "...................." *

*Insert Pet Name here, or why not
make up a really awful new one?

"Do not be AFRAID for the Great Hand will GUIDE you."

"But whose is The Hand and WHERE will it TAKE me?"

"It is the Hand of all HUMANITY. It is the GOOD within us all. It crosses all religions and beliefs. It is The Great HAND of LOVE.

HOLD it and ALL WILL BE WELL."

The Great HAND of LOVE

Cut this out and stick it on
your HEAD - then everyone
will know what I think
of you*

* but please don't blame me if
  you get some funny looks.
  People can be WEIRD, you know.

YOUR SPECIAL LOVE STICKER

SOMEBODY   THINKS

I'M GORGEOUS

Together, Master of all knowledge and Student of Life gaze at the giant Sponge Cake.

STUDENT: What is this overwhelming feeling of **PEACE** and **HARMONY**, oh **MASTER**? From where does it come?

MASTER: It comes, my Child, not from the sponges themselves but from the **SPACE** that lies **BETWEEN** them. For what holds them **TOGETHER** is not just the Cream of **DESIRE**...

(DRAMATIC PAUSE)

... but the glorious Jam of **FRIENDSHIP** as well.

The SECRET of TRUE LOVE

COME DANCE into the STREETS

Come DANCE into the streets with me
For in the skies above
Shine the Brassière of Fortune
And the Underpants of Love

THE ONLY WAY

MY DARLING

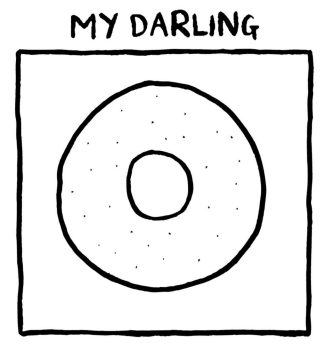

You are the DOUGHNUT
of my DESIRE

MY LOVE

I've stuck my LOVE upon a stick
For you to come and take a lick
And should the taste with you agree
Oh, how HAPPY I shall be!

* But I am not very good at DRAWING Human Beings so I have drawn a POTATO instead. But the potato is very BEAUTIFUL too - in its own way

YOU are a BEAUTIFUL
HUMAN BEING*

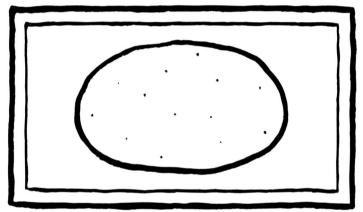

For every person in the world, there is one other SPECIAL person who they are DESTINED to meet and SHARE their life with.

Being pretty anal, I thought I would have to check EVERY SINGLE person in the world to MAKE SURE that I got the RIGHT one. But when I found ·YOU· I KNEW that I could stop.

I guess you know how UNBELIEVABLY WONDERFUL that makes you.

I mean, you know what I'M LIKE...

ROMANTIC MESSAGE
from a CONTROL FREAK

Their **LOVE** for each other does not diminish.

Instead it grows **STRONGER** and more **BEAUTIFUL** as each year passes.

The BISCUITS of LOVE

Lady Biscuit   Man Biscuit

YOU ARE LOVELY

May flowers of HAPPINESS endlessly GROW in the sweet ENCHANTED garden of your HEART